Teagan's Butterflies

Published in the UK by Scholastic Education, 2022
Scholastic Distribution Centre, Bosworth Avenue, Tournament Fields, Warwick, CV34 6UQ
Scholastic Ireland, 89E Lagan Road, Dublin Industrial Estate, Glasnevin, Dublin, D11 HP5F

SCHOLASTIC and associated logos are trademarks and/or registered trademarks of Scholastic Inc.
www.scholastic.co.uk
© 2022 Scholastic
123456789 2345678901

Printed by Ashford Colour Press
The book is made of materials from well-managed, FSC®-certified forests and other controlled sources.

A CIP catalogue record for this book is available from the British Library.

ISBN 978-0702-30911-3

All rights reserved. This book is sold subject to the condition that it shall not, by way of trade or otherwise, be lent, hired out or otherwise circulated in any form of binding or cover other than that in which it is published. No part of this publication may be reproduced, stored in a retrieval system, or transmitted in any form or by any other means (electronic, mechanical, photocopying, recording or otherwise) without prior written permission of Scholastic Limited.

Every effort has been made to trace copyright holders for the works reproduced in this publication, and the publishers apologise for any inadvertent omissions.

Author
Catherine Baker
Editorial team
Rachel Morgan, Vicki Yates, Fiona Undrill, Jennie Clifford
Design team
Dipa Mistry, Justin Hoffmann, Andrea Lewis, We Are Grace
Illustrations
Debby Rahmalia/The Bright Agency

Help your child to read!

This book practises these letters and letter sounds.
Point and say the sounds with your child:

- ay (as in 'away')
- ou (as in 'out')
- ea (as in 'leaf')
- ir (as in 'girls')
- ie (as in 'lie')
- ue (as in 'blue')

Your child may need help to read these common tricky words:

- was
- she
- the
- said
- they
- of
- to
- put
- all
- like
- some
- into
- full
- were

Before reading
- Look at the cover picture and read the title together. Read the back cover blurb to your child.
- Ask your child: *What is Teagan doing in the picture?*

During reading
- If your child gets stuck on a word, remind them to sound it out and then blend the sounds to read the word: b-ir-th-d-ay, birthday.
- If they are still stuck, show them how to read the word.
- Enjoy looking at the pictures together. Pause to talk about the story.

After reading
- Ask your child: *What did the caterpillars eat? What did they turn into before they became butterflies?*
- *How do you think Teagan felt at the end of the story? Why?*

It was Teagan's birthday. She got a music box from Gran, and a unicorn T-shirt from her big sister, Bea.

But Teagan's best birthday present was...

...a net! It sounds odd, but it's true.

The net was from Mum. It was for keeping caterpillars in.

Teagan and Bea looked for caterpillars in the garden.

"It's the right season," said Mum. "Look on each leaf."

Bea found six caterpillars.
"That's fantastic, girls!" said Mum.

They found lots of green stuff for the caterpillars to lie on and eat.

Mum helped Teagan set up the net. Teagan put a sheet on the ground.

Mum put all the green stuff in a pot. "This is caterpillar fuel!" she said.

"Caterpillars like the damp," said Mum. Teagan sprayed the air.

They put in some sticks, too.

Teagan waited three weeks.
The caterpillars had eaten a lot!

They turned into cocoons, hanging on the sticks.

The next Tuesday, Teagan looked in the net.
"Mum! Bea!" she shouted. "Butterflies!"

It was true. The net was full of Peacock butterflies.
They were bright red, black and blue.

Teagan took the net out in the garden. Out fluttered a cloud of butterflies.

Teagan felt proud as her birthday butterflies drifted away.

Retell the story